MY DYSFUNCTIONS

KNOCK
KNOCK®
VENICE, CALIFORNIA

Created and published by Knock Knock
Distributed by Who's There Inc.
Venice, CA 90291
knockknockstuff.com

ISBN: 978-160106341-0
UPC: 825703-50075-2

10 9 8 7 6 5 4

WE ALL HAVE
ISSUES

The idea that anyone has it together is a myth—despite the occasional deliberately constructed appearance to the contrary. The only thing that separates the men from the boys and the women from the girls is self-awareness. Do you or do you not know that you're half-crazy? Do you celebrate and process your dysfunctions or do you stumble along in blithe denial—or, perhaps, the stubborn refusal to deal?

Either way, being dysfunctional is the norm, not the exception, especially in this era of pop psychology and antidepressant ads littered with daisies and sunshine. I'm not okay and you're not okay, and there's a drug for that. Now that we know how to diagnose and name it, 29 percent of the American population has experienced a significant episode of anxiety, while about 15 percent will suffer from a major depression at some point. In 2008, the American self-help industry—including books, recordings, seminars, and coaching—was $11 billion strong. What are we if not dysfunctional?

Though medical professionals first used the term "neurosis" in the mid–nineteenth century, "dysfunction" was not associated with psychology until the 1950s. The rise of the contemporary self-help movement in the late 1970s cemented our knowledge that we're all abnormal. We have at our disposal a delectable variety of ways to be dysfunctional, including anxiety, depression, phobias, post-traumatic stress disorder, and plain old kookiness. Most of us come from dysfunctional families, and we're likely either to repeat our parents' dysfunctions or to manifest new ones as a result of accommodating them.

On the brighter side, dysfunction makes us interesting. Notably brilliant—and neurotic—artists include Salvador Dalí, Charles Dickens, and, of course, Woody Allen. One study found that people who'd achieved recognition for their accomplishments had a slightly higher percentage of psychological problems than the general population, with visual artists and writers pulling way ahead of the pack; 75 percent and 90 percent, respectively, suffer mental disturbances. According to Marcel Proust, "Everything great in the world comes from neurotics."

But as creatively valuable as our dysfunctions may be, we must manage them in order to live a practical and not entirely miserable existence. Toward that end, our most convenient, accessible tool is surely a journal. Kathleen Adams, founder of the Center for Journal Therapy, calls journals "79-cent therapists." According to a widely cited study by James W. Pennebaker and Janel D. Seagal, "Writing about important personal experiences in an emotional way for as little as fifteen minutes over the course of three days brings about improvements in mental and physical health." Proven benefits include stress management, strengthened immunity, fewer doctor visits, and improvement in chronic illnesses such as asthma. "It's hard to believe," says Pennebaker, a psychology professor at the University of Texas at Austin, but "being able to put experiences into words is good for your physical health."

How does this work? Some experts believe organizing our experience into a narrative may be beneficial. According to scholarship cited in *Newsweek*, journaling "forces us to transform the ruminations cluttering our minds into coherent stories. Writing about an experience may also dull its emotional impact." Psychologist Ira Progoff, the father of the modern journaling movement, once observed that an "intensive journal process" could "draw each person's life toward wholeness at its own tempo."

To get the most out of the process, here are a few tips: experts agree that you should try to write quasi-daily, for at least 5–15 minutes. For inspiration, famed diarist Anaïs Nin suggests asking yourself, "What feels vivid, warm, or near to you at the moment?" Don't critique your writing; just spew. Finally, determine a home for your journal where others won't find it.

As someone who proudly recognizes your dysfunctions, you've chosen a journal that honestly states its purpose. Use this repository to reflect the true you—neuroses, sarcasm, insanity, and all. Go forth and dysfunction!

Sanity is a cozy lie.

Susan Sontag

DATE

WHY I AM DYSFUNCTIONAL TODAY:

_____

_____

_____

_____

_____

_____

_____

_____

_____

_____

_____

_____

_____

_____

_____

_____

_____

WHAT WOULD MAKE IT BETTER TODAY:

I believe that everybody comes from pain and a certain amount of dysfunction.

Mariel Hemingway

WHY I AM DYSFUNCTIONAL TODAY:

_____

_____

_____

_____

_____

_____

_____

_____

_____

_____

_____

_____

_____

_____

_____

_____

_____

_____

WHAT WOULD MAKE IT BETTER TODAY:

I know I'm paranoid
and neurotic; I've made
a career out of it.

Thom Yorke

WHY I AM DYSFUNCTIONAL TODAY:

_____

_____

_____

_____

_____

_____

_____

_____

_____

_____

_____

_____

_____

_____

_____

_____

WHAT WOULD MAKE IT BETTER TODAY:

The advantage of the emotions is that they lead us astray.

Oscar Wilde

WHY I AM DYSFUNCTIONAL TODAY:

_____
_____
_____
_____
_____
_____
_____
_____
_____
_____
_____
_____
_____
_____
_____
_____
_____
_____

WHAT WOULD MAKE IT BETTER TODAY:

Instant gratification takes too long.

Carrie Fisher

DATE		

WHY I AM DYSFUNCTIONAL TODAY:

_____

_____

_____

_____

_____

_____

_____

_____

_____

_____

_____

_____

_____

_____

_____

_____

_____

_____

WHAT WOULD MAKE IT BETTER TODAY:

The statistics on sanity are that one out of every four Americans is suffering from some form of mental illness. Think of your three best friends. If they're okay, then it's you.

Rita Mae Brown

WHY I AM DYSFUNCTIONAL TODAY:

_____

_____

_____

_____

_____

_____

_____

_____

_____

_____

_____

_____

_____

_____

_____

_____

_____

_____

WHAT WOULD MAKE IT BETTER TODAY:

The average, healthy, well-adjusted adult gets up at seven-thirty in the morning feeling just plain terrible.

Jean Kerr

DATE

WHY I AM DYSFUNCTIONAL TODAY:

_____

_____

_____

_____

_____

_____

_____

_____

_____

_____

_____

_____

_____

_____

_____

_____

_____

WHAT WOULD MAKE IT BETTER TODAY:

It's not denial. I'm just selective about the reality I accept.

Bill Watterson

DATE

WHY I AM DYSFUNCTIONAL TODAY:

_____

_____

_____

_____

_____

_____

_____

_____

_____

_____

_____

_____

_____

_____

_____

_____

_____

WHAT WOULD MAKE IT BETTER TODAY:

A happy childhood
is poor preparation
for human contacts.

Colette

DATE

WHY I AM DYSFUNCTIONAL TODAY:

_____

_____

_____

_____

_____

_____

_____

_____

_____

_____

_____

_____

_____

_____

_____

_____

_____

WHAT WOULD MAKE IT BETTER TODAY:

For me, insanity is super sanity.
The normal is psychotic.
Normal means lack of imagination,
lack of creativity.

Jean Dubuffet

DATE

WHY I AM DYSFUNCTIONAL TODAY:

_____

_____

_____

_____

_____

_____

_____

_____

_____

_____

_____

_____

_____

_____

_____

_____

WHAT WOULD MAKE IT BETTER TODAY:

When all else fails there's always delusion.

Conan O'Brien

DATE

WHY I AM DYSFUNCTIONAL TODAY:

WHAT WOULD MAKE IT BETTER TODAY:

I prefer neurotic people.
I like to hear rumblings
beneath the surface.

Stephen Sondheim

DATE

WHY I AM DYSFUNCTIONAL TODAY:

Men can only be happy when they do not assume that the object of life is happiness.

George Orwell

WHY I AM DYSFUNCTIONAL TODAY:

_____

_____

_____

_____

_____

_____

_____

_____

_____

_____

_____

_____

_____

_____

_____

_____

_____

_____

WHAT WOULD MAKE IT BETTER TODAY:

We all live in a house on fire, no fire department to call; no way out, just the upstairs window to look out of while the fire burns the house down with us trapped, locked in it.

Tennessee Williams

DATE		

WHY I AM DYSFUNCTIONAL TODAY:

_____

_____

_____

_____

_____

_____

_____

_____

_____

_____

_____

_____

_____

_____

_____

_____

_____

WHAT WOULD MAKE IT BETTER TODAY:

There is only one difference between a madman and me. I am not mad.

Salvador Dali

DATE

WHY I AM DYSFUNCTIONAL TODAY:

_____

_____

_____

_____

_____

_____

_____

_____

_____

_____

_____

_____

_____

_____

_____

_____

_____

WHAT WOULD MAKE IT BETTER TODAY:

They say best men are molded
out of faults, and, for the most,
become much more the better
for being a little bad.

William Shakespeare

WHY I AM DYSFUNCTIONAL TODAY:

_____

_____

_____

_____

_____

_____

_____

_____

_____

_____

_____

_____

_____

_____

_____

_____

WHAT WOULD MAKE IT BETTER TODAY.

I cry a lot. My emotions are very close to my surface. I don't want to hold anything in so it festers and turns into pus—a pustule of emotion that explodes into a festering cesspool of depression.

Nicolas Cage

WHY I AM DYSFUNCTIONAL TODAY:

_____

_____

_____

_____

_____

_____

_____

_____

_____

_____

_____

_____

_____

_____

_____

_____

WHAT WOULD MAKE IT BETTER TODAY:

You're nuts, but you're welcome here.

Steve Martin

DATE		

WHY I AM DYSFUNCTIONAL TODAY:

_____

_____

_____

_____

_____

_____

_____

_____

_____

_____

_____

_____

_____

_____

_____

_____

_____

WHAT WOULD MAKE IT BETTER TODAY:

If neurotic is wanting two mutually exclusive things at one and the same time, then I'm neurotic as hell. I'll be flying back and forth between one mutually exclusive thing and another for the rest of my days.

Sylvia Plath

WHY I AM DYSFUNCTIONAL TODAY:

_____

_____

_____

_____

_____

_____

_____

_____

_____

_____

_____

_____

_____

_____

_____

_____

WHAT WOULD MAKE IT BETTER TODAY:

I've been the queen of dysfunction and made every mistake one can make.

Janice Dickinson

WHY I AM DYSFUNCTIONAL TODAY:

_____

_____

_____

_____

_____

_____

_____

_____

_____

_____

_____

_____

_____

_____

_____

_____

WHAT WOULD MAKE IT BETTER TODAY:

All are lunatics, but he who
can analyze his delusion is
called a philosopher.

Ambrose Bierce

DATE

WHY I AM DYSFUNCTIONAL TODAY:

_____

_____

_____

_____

_____

_____

_____

_____

_____

_____

_____

_____

_____

_____

_____

WHAT WOULD MAKE IT BETTER TODAY:

Sin, guilt, neurosis—they are one and the same, the fruit of the tree of knowledge.

Henry Miller

WHY I AM DYSFUNCTIONAL TODAY:

WHAT WOULD MAKE IT BETTER TODAY:

I have cultivated my
hysteria with pleasure
and terror.

Charles Baudelaire

DATE

WHY I AM DYSFUNCTIONAL TODAY:

_____

_____

_____

_____

_____

_____

_____

_____

_____

_____

_____

_____

_____

_____

_____

_____

_____

_____

WHAT WOULD MAKE IT BETTER TODAY:

You can get the monkey off your back, but the circus never leaves town.

Anne Lamott

WHY I AM DYSFUNCTIONAL TODAY:

WHAT WOULD MAKE IT BETTER TODAY:

Oh, the nerves, the nerves; the mysteries of this machine called Man! Oh, the little that unhinges it; poor creatures that we are!

Charles Dickens

DATE

WHY I AM DYSFUNCTIONAL TODAY:

_____

_____

_____

_____

_____

_____

_____

_____

_____

_____

_____

_____

_____

_____

_____

_____

WHAT WOULD MAKE IT BETTER TODAY:

I told the doctor I was overtired, anxiety ridden, compulsively active, constantly depressed, with recurring fits of paranoia. Turns out I'm normal.

Jules Feiffer

WHY I AM DYSFUNCTIONAL TODAY:

_____

_____

_____

_____

_____

_____

_____

_____

_____

_____

_____

_____

_____

_____

_____

_____

WHAT WOULD MAKE IT BETTER TODAY:

If you can go through life without ever experiencing pain you probably haven't been born yet.

Neil Simon

DATE

WHY I AM DYSFUNCTIONAL TODAY:

_____

_____

_____

_____

_____

_____

_____

_____

_____

_____

_____

_____

_____

_____

_____

_____

_____

WHAT WOULD MAKE IT BETTER TODAY:

I've always loathed rich people, so I've become a person who I've loathed. And I loathed myself even when I wasn't that person, which makes it doubly difficult, if you can follow all that.

Larry David

DATE

WHY I AM DYSFUNCTIONAL TODAY:

_____

_____

_____

_____

_____

_____

_____

_____

_____

_____

_____

_____

_____

_____

_____

WHAT WOULD MAKE IT BETTER TODAY:

I have
a very
highly
developed
sense of
denial.

Gwyneth Paltrow

DATE		

WHY I AM DYSFUNCTIONAL TODAY:

_____

_____

_____

_____

_____

_____

_____

_____

_____

_____

_____

_____

_____

_____

_____

_____

_____

WHAT WOULD MAKE IT BETTER TODAY:

It is much more comfortable to be mad and know it than be sane and have one's doubts.

G. B. Burgin

DATE

WHY I AM DYSFUNCTIONAL TODAY:

_____

_____

_____

_____

_____

_____

_____

_____

_____

_____

_____

_____

_____

_____

_____

_____

_____

WHAT WOULD MAKE IT BETTER TODAY:

Feelings are not supposed to be logical. Dangerous is the man who has rationalized his emotions.

David Borenstein

DATE		

WHY I AM DYSFUNCTIONAL TODAY:

_____

_____

_____

_____

_____

_____

_____

_____

_____

_____

_____

_____

_____

_____

_____

_____

_____

_____

WHAT WOULD MAKE IT BETTER TODAY:

It's all right letting yourself go, as long as you can get yourself back.

Mick Jagger

DATE

WHY I AM DYSFUNCTIONAL TODAY:

_____

_____

_____

_____

_____

_____

_____

_____

_____

_____

_____

_____

_____

_____

_____

_____

_____

_____

WHAT WOULD MAKE IT BETTER TODAY:

I'm afraid of making a mistake. I'm not totally neurotic, but I'm pretty neurotic about it. I'm as close to totally neurotic as you can get without being totally neurotic.

Bridget Fonda

DATE

WHY I AM DYSFUNCTIONAL TODAY:

_____

_____

_____

_____

_____

_____

_____

_____

_____

_____

_____

_____

_____

_____

_____

_____

_____

WHAT WOULD MAKE IT BETTER TODAY:

I believe in looking reality straight in the eye and denying it.

Garrison Keillor

WHY I AM DYSFUNCTIONAL TODAY:

_____

_____

_____

_____

_____

_____

_____

_____

_____

_____

_____

_____

_____

_____

_____

_____

_____

WHAT WOULD MAKE IT BETTER TODAY:

Insane people are always sure they're just fine. It's only the sane people who are willing to admit they're crazy.

Nora Ephron

WHY I AM DYSFUNCTIONAL TODAY:

_____

_____

_____

_____

_____

_____

_____

_____

_____

_____

_____

_____

_____

_____

_____

_____

WHAT WOULD MAKE IT BETTER TODAY:

I can sympathize with people's pains, but not with their pleasures. There is something curiously boring about somebody else's happiness.

Aldous Huxley

DATE

WHY I AM DYSFUNCTIONAL TODAY:

_____

_____

_____

_____

_____

_____

_____

_____

_____

_____

_____

_____

_____

_____

_____

_____

_____

WHAT WOULD MAKE IT BETTER TODAY:

Friends love misery, in fact. Sometimes, especially if we are too lucky or too successful or too pretty, our misery is the only thing that endears us to our friends.

Erica Jong

DATE

WHY I AM DYSFUNCTIONAL TODAY:

_____

_____

_____

_____

_____

_____

_____

_____

_____

_____

_____

_____

_____

_____

_____

_____

WHAT WOULD MAKE IT BETTER TODAY:

He who despises himself
nevertheless esteems
himself as a self-despiser.

Friedrich Nietzsche

WHY I AM DYSFUNCTIONAL TODAY:

_____

_____

_____

_____

_____

_____

_____

_____

_____

_____

_____

_____

_____

_____

_____

_____

WHAT WOULD MAKE IT BETTER TODAY:

"Know thyself"? If I knew myself, I'd run away.

Johann Wolfgang von Goethe

DATE

WHY I AM DYSFUNCTIONAL TODAY:

_____

_____

_____

_____

_____

_____

_____

_____

_____

_____

_____

_____

_____

_____

_____

_____

_____

WHAT WOULD MAKE IT BETTER TODAY:

If we cannot be happy
and powerful and prey
on others, we invent
conscience and prey
on ourselves.

Elbert Hubbard

DATE

WHY I AM DYSFUNCTIONAL TODAY:

_____

_____

_____

_____

_____

_____

_____

_____

_____

_____

_____

_____

_____

_____

_____

WHAT WOULD MAKE IT BETTER TODAY:

I know whenever it comes to
be really dysfunctional and vile
and base and hostile on screen,
I'm good at that!

Werner Herzog

DATE

WHY I AM DYSFUNCTIONAL TODAY:

_____

_____

_____

_____

_____

_____

_____

_____

_____

_____

_____

_____

_____

_____

_____

_____

WHAT WOULD MAKE IT BETTER TODAY:

It is sometimes an appropriate response to reality to go insane.

Philip K. Dick

WHY I AM DYSFUNCTIONAL TODAY:

_____
_____
_____
_____
_____
_____
_____
_____
_____
_____
_____
_____
_____
_____
_____
_____
_____
_____

WHAT WOULD MAKE IT BETTER TODAY:

Everything great in the world comes from neurotics. They alone have founded our religions and composed our masterpieces.

Marcel Proust

WHY I AM DYSFUNCTIONAL TODAY:

_____

_____

_____

_____

_____

_____

_____

_____

_____

_____

_____

_____

_____

_____

WHAT WOULD MAKE IT BETTER TODAY:

It's crazy how you can get yourself in a mess sometimes and not even be able to think about it with any sense and yet not be able to think about anything else.

Stanley Kubrick

WHY I AM DYSFUNCTIONAL TODAY:

_____

_____

_____

_____

_____

_____

_____

_____

_____

_____

_____

_____

_____

_____

_____

_____

_____

WHAT WOULD MAKE IT BETTER TODAY:

Delusions of grandeur make me feel a lot better about myself.

Lily Tomlin

DATE

WHY I AM DYSFUNCTIONAL TODAY:

_____

_____

_____

_____

_____

_____

_____

_____

_____

_____

_____

_____

_____

_____

WHAT WOULD MAKE IT BETTER TODAY:

A life based on reason will always require to be balanced by an occasional bout of violent and irrational emotion, for the instinctual drives must be satisfied.

Cyril Connolly

DATE

WHY I AM DYSFUNCTIONAL TODAY:

WHAT WOULD MAKE IT BETTER TODAY:

I always say shopping is
cheaper than a psychiatrist.

Tammy Faye Bakker

DATE		

WHY I AM DYSFUNCTIONAL TODAY:

_____

_____

_____

_____

_____

_____

_____

_____

_____

_____

_____

_____

_____

_____

_____

_____

_____

WHAT WOULD MAKE IT BETTER TODAY:

If my devils are to leave me, I am afraid my angels will take flight as well.

Rainer Maria Rilke

WHY I AM DYSFUNCTIONAL TODAY:

_____

_____

_____

_____

_____

_____

_____

_____

_____

_____

_____

_____

_____

_____

_____

_____

_____

_____

WHAT WOULD MAKE IT BETTER TODAY:

You may be right
I may be crazy
But it just may be
a lunatic you're
looking for.

Billy Joel

DATE

WHY I AM DYSFUNCTIONAL TODAY:

_____

_____

_____

_____

_____

_____

_____

_____

_____

_____

_____

_____

_____

_____

_____

_____

_____

WHAT WOULD MAKE IT BETTER TODAY:

Denial ain't just a river in Egypt.

Mark Twain

DATE

WHY I AM DYSFUNCTIONAL TODAY:

_____

_____

_____

_____

_____

_____

_____

_____

_____

_____

_____

_____

_____

_____

_____

_____

_____

WHAT WOULD MAKE IT BETTER TODAY:

A certain degree
of neurosis is of
inestimable value
as a drive, especially
to a psychologist.

Sigmund Freud

DATE		

WHY I AM DYSFUNCTIONAL TODAY:

_____

_____

_____

_____

_____

_____

_____

_____

_____

_____

_____

_____

_____

_____

_____

_____

_____

_____

WHAT WOULD MAKE IT BETTER TODAY:

See, the human mind is kind of like ... a piñata. When it breaks open, there's a lot of surprises inside. Once you get the piñata perspective, you see that losing your mind can be a peak experience.

Jane Wagner

WHY I AM DYSFUNCTIONAL TODAY:

_____

_____

_____

_____

_____

_____

_____

_____

_____

_____

_____

_____

_____

_____

_____

WHAT WOULD MAKE IT BETTER TODAY:

I wouldn't recommend sex, drugs, or insanity for everyone, but they've always worked for me.

Hunter S. Thompson

WHY I AM DYSFUNCTIONAL TODAY:

_____

_____

_____

_____

_____

_____

_____

_____

_____

_____

_____

_____

_____

_____

_____

WHAT WOULD MAKE IT BETTER TODAY:

Perhaps the only true dignity of man is his capacity to despise himself.

George Santayana

WHY I AM DYSFUNCTIONAL TODAY:

_____

_____

_____

_____

_____

_____

_____

_____

_____

_____

_____

_____

_____

_____

_____

_____

_____

WHAT WOULD MAKE IT BETTER TODAY:

All successful people these days seem to be neurotic. Perhaps we should stop being sorry for them and start being sorry for me—for being so confounded normal.

Deborah Kerr

WHY I AM DYSFUNCTIONAL TODAY:

_____

_____

_____

_____

_____

_____

_____

_____

_____

_____

_____

_____

_____

_____

_____

WHAT WOULD MAKE IT BETTER TODAY:

In a well-run mental household there ought to be a thorough cleaning at the threshold of consciousness a few times a year.

Karl Kraus

DATE

WHY I AM DYSFUNCTIONAL TODAY:

_____

_____

_____

_____

_____

_____

_____

_____

_____

_____

_____

_____

_____

_____

_____

_____

WHAT WOULD MAKE IT BETTER TODAY:

I exist
in a state
of almost
perpetual
hysteria.

Sting

DATE		

WHY I AM DYSFUNCTIONAL TODAY:

_____

_____

_____

_____

_____

_____

_____

_____

_____

_____

_____

_____

_____

_____

_____

_____

_____

WHAT WOULD MAKE IT BETTER TODAY:

The good die young—because
they see it's no use living if
you've got to be good.

John Barrymore

WHY I AM DYSFUNCTIONAL TODAY:

WHAT WOULD MAKE IT BETTER TODAY:

I was the captain of the latent paranoid softball team. We used to play all the neurotics on Sunday morning. The nail biters against the bed wetters. But if you've never seen neurotics play softball, it's really funny. I used to steal second base, then feel guilty and go back.

Woody Allen

DATE

WHY I AM DYSFUNCTIONAL TODAY:

_____

_____

_____

_____

_____

_____

_____

_____

_____

_____

_____

_____

_____

_____

_____

_____

_____

WHAT WOULD MAKE IT BETTER TODAY:

There is no great genius without tincture of madness.

Seneca

DATE		

WHY I AM DYSFUNCTIONAL TODAY:

_____

_____

_____

_____

_____

_____

_____

_____

_____

_____

_____

_____

_____

_____

_____

WHAT WOULD MAKE IT BETTER TODAY:

There's a fine line between genius and insanity. I have erased this line.

Oscar Levant

DATE

WHY I AM DYSFUNCTIONAL TODAY:

_____

_____

_____

_____

_____

_____

_____

_____

_____

_____

_____

_____

_____

_____

_____

_____

_____

WHAT WOULD MAKE IT BETTER TODAY:

I'm a neurotic—in the sense that I live in *my* world. I will not adjust myself to *the* world. I am adjusted to myself.

Anaïs Nin

DATE

WHY I AM DYSFUNCTIONAL TODAY:

WHAT WOULD MAKE IT BETTER TODAY:

Doubt is not a pleasant
condition, but certainty
is an absurd one.

Voltaire

DATE		

WHY I AM DYSFUNCTIONAL TODAY:

_____

_____

_____

_____

_____

_____

_____

_____

_____

_____

_____

_____

_____

_____

_____

_____

_____

WHAT WOULD MAKE IT BETTER TODAY:

Happiness is having a large, loving, caring, close-knit family in another city.

George Burns

DATE

WHY I AM DYSFUNCTIONAL TODAY:

_____

_____

_____

_____

_____

_____

_____

_____

_____

_____

_____

_____

_____

_____

_____

_____

_____

WHAT WOULD MAKE IT BETTER TODAY:

You're only given a little spark
of madness. You mustn't lose it.

Robin Williams

WHY I AM DYSFUNCTIONAL TODAY:

_____

_____

_____

_____

_____

_____

_____

_____

_____

_____

_____

_____

_____

_____

_____

_____

_____

_____

WHAT WOULD MAKE IT BETTER TODAY:

Some people never go crazy. What truly horrible lives they must live.

Charles Bukowski

WHY I AM DYSFUNCTIONAL TODAY:

_____

_____

_____

_____

_____

_____

_____

_____

_____

_____

_____

_____

_____

_____

_____

_____

_____

_____

WHAT WOULD MAKE IT BETTER TODAY:

There is a luxury in self-reproach. When we blame ourselves we feel no one else has a right to blame us.

Oscar Wilde

WHY I AM DYSFUNCTIONAL TODAY:

WHAT WOULD MAKE IT BETTER TODAY:

If you commit a big crime then
you are crazy, and the more heinous
the crime the crazier you must be.
Therefore you are not responsible,
and nothing is your fault.

Peggy Noonan

DATE

WHY I AM DYSFUNCTIONAL TODAY:

_____

_____

_____

_____

_____

_____

_____

_____

_____

_____

_____

_____

_____

_____

_____

_____

WHAT WOULD MAKE IT BETTER TODAY:

The final delusion is the belief that one has lost all delusions.

Maurice Chapelain

DATE

WHY I AM DYSFUNCTIONAL TODAY:

_____

_____

_____

_____

_____

_____

_____

_____

_____

_____

_____

_____

_____

_____

_____

_____

_____

WHAT WOULD MAKE IT BETTER TODAY:

Hope—in reality it is the worst
of all evils, because it prolongs
the torments of man.

Friedrich Nietzsche

DATE

WHY I AM DYSFUNCTIONAL TODAY:

_____

_____

_____

_____

_____

_____

_____

_____

_____

_____

_____

_____

_____

_____

WHAT WOULD MAKE IT BETTER TODAY:

When we remember
that we are all
mad, the mysteries
disappear and life
stands explained.

Mark Twain

WHY I AM DYSFUNCTIONAL TODAY:

_____

_____

_____

_____

_____

_____

_____

_____

_____

_____

_____

_____

_____

_____

_____

_____

WHAT WOULD MAKE IT BETTER TODAY:

To be too conscious is an illness—
a real thoroughgoing illness.

Fyodor Dostoevsky

WHY I AM DYSFUNCTIONAL TODAY:

_____

_____

_____

_____

_____

_____

_____

_____

_____

_____

_____

_____

_____

_____

_____

_____

_____

_____

WHAT WOULD MAKE IT BETTER TODAY:

I became
insane,
with long
intervals
of horrible
sanity.

Edgar Allan Poe

WHY I AM DYSFUNCTIONAL TODAY:

_____

_____

_____

_____

_____

_____

_____

_____

_____

_____

_____

_____

_____

_____

_____

_____

_____

WHAT WOULD MAKE IT BETTER TODAY:

Self-pity—it's the only
pity that counts.

Oscar Levant

WHY I AM DYSFUNCTIONAL TODAY:

_____

_____

_____

_____

_____

_____

_____

_____

_____

_____

_____

_____

_____

_____

_____

_____

_____

WHAT WOULD MAKE IT BETTER TODAY:

I don't know why we are here,
but I'm pretty sure that it is not
in order to enjoy ourselves.

Ludwig Wittgenstein

WHY I AM DYSFUNCTIONAL TODAY:

_____

_____

_____

_____

_____

_____

_____

_____

_____

_____

_____

_____

_____

_____

_____

_____

_____

WHAT WOULD MAKE IT BETTER TODAY:

All men should strive to learn
   before they die

what they are running from,
   and to, and why.

James Thurber

DATE

WHY I AM DYSFUNCTIONAL TODAY:

WHAT WOULD MAKE IT BETTER TODAY:

We're more interesting if we are dysfunctional.

Rupert Everett

DATE

WHY I AM DYSFUNCTIONAL TODAY:

_____

_____

_____

_____

_____

_____

_____

_____

_____

_____

_____

_____

_____

_____

_____

_____

_____

_____

WHAT WOULD MAKE IT BETTER TODAY:

It's not my fault.

Knock Knock